1001
KNIGHTS

VOL II FELLOWSHIP

With Foreword by Rebecca and Steven Sugar

THE GREAT WINDMILL

1001 Knights Curated by Annie Stoll & Kevin Jay Stanton
Art Direction & Design by Annie Stoll
Cover Illustration & Crest by Kevin Jay Stanton

1001 Knights is a 3 volume people-positive anthology.
There are over 260 artists who participated in *1001 Knights*.
The book in your hands is Vol. II, Fellowship.

1001 Knights was made possible by our generous Kickstarter backers.
Please visit our website to view a full list of their names at
www.OneThousandAndOneKnights.com/thankyou

Thank you to all the amazing artists. We hope that you, dear reader, check each of them out in the index & discover new and amazing worlds of art. Special thank you to the team who helped us created 1001 Knights: George Rohac & the Breadpig team, T.H., Shariq Ansari, Matt Pichette, Lillian Skye, & all our friends and family for believing in all of us and helping us make this project a reality.

Typefaces:
DropCaps are Ivory by Facetype Foundry. Ivory is inspired by a beautiful typeface used in an illustrated compendium about pomology from 1882. Body copy is Begum by Indian Type Foundry. The complete Begum super family was designed in India by Manushi Parikh. Logotype is based on Charcuterie Block a typeface created by Laura Worthington. Charcuterie is an homage to the inventiveness, passion, and care of peasants who proudly handed down recipes through generations.

First Printing, 2017

ISBN 978-0-9988204-1-5

www.OneThousandAndOneKnights.com | OneThousandAndOneKnights@gmail.com

"When we love, we always strive to become better than we are. When we strive to become better than we are, everything around us becomes better too."

—PAULO COELHO,
"THE ALCHEMIST"

1001 KNIGHTS is a people-positive project that started out as a small zine and grew into so much more. Years in the making, there are more than 260 artists and over 3,000 Kickstarter backers who made this book possible. When 1001 Knights was first conceived, we vowed that all artists were welcome regardless of gender, sexual identity, race, creed, or nationality.

The only question posed was "What does it mean to be a knight?" And we will let you, dear reader, enjoy and be inspired by the incredible imagination of the artists of 1001 Knights...

TABLE OF CONTENTS

FOREWORD

Devotion and dedication, loyalty and passion, and all the gorgeous hallmarks of a knight will always be so appealing, but as siblings who both love to write and draw, these days we like to mix that with the truth of our experience.

We've been working together since we were kids. We always loved to brainstorm and draw to come up with elaborate plans for novels and comic books and tarot decks and video games and anything else we could think of. We'd try to figure out each others' sensibility and support the differences in what we wanted to do. But we both loved stories about knights! Righteousness, martyrdom, chivalry, romance! We were both drawn to the kind of hero that would devote themselves entirely to a cause the way we wanted to devote ourselves entirely to drawing!

When we started working in the animation industry building a story and a world from the ground up together, the kind of teamwork we'd practiced growing up suddenly became the backbone of our project, and the meat of it became all the themes we'd loved to explore! But the more we worked on it together, the less the chivalrous martyr knight seemed romantic, and the more righteous teamwork became. We wanted to argue and problem solve as equals, we wanted to fight for each other and protect each other, and instead of giving direction and taking it we wanted to find a direction together, one that could change as we changed.

The way we thought about the knight archetype changed, because throwing yourself head first into something someone else told you to believe started to seem careless or even self destructive. Heading clear-eyed toward the unknown, surrounded by people to trust and learn from, seemed much more beautiful and true.

Devotion and passion are better served alongside the honest supportive feedback and the dependable encouragement one can only get from working together. Trust, growth, and companionship are more powerful than service and sovereignty, and just as heroic! Lead and follow, teach and learn, take care of yourself and others.

— REBECCA AND STEVEN SUGAR

The Lammergeier is an Old World vulture species found throughout the high mountains. Its aliases — "Ossifrage" in Old English and "Quebrantahuesos" in Spanish — both mean "bone breaker." This refers to its habit of dropping bones from soaring heights onto the rocky ground below in order to crack them into pieces and expose the nutritious marrow inside. It takes a young Lammergeier seven years to perfect this skill. While vultures are carrion eaters and therefore are not, as a rule, used for falconry, some of the high desert tribeswomen have developed a use for these birds. As juveniles, they are trained to carry stones or fire-bombs in their talons and drop them onto enemy tribes. An experienced adult Lammergeier can accurately hit a target from a height of over 500 feet, well beyond the range of retaliatory fire.

Is it supposed to do...

...this?

Someone owes me $10.

WOOOO! YEAH!

Looks like the game is a different dimension.

We probably have to beat it to go home.

This world is a magical place.

Not just this game world but the real world too...

Filled with amazing things...

...and terrible things.

Sometimes I question everything I know.

Think I can eat this?

You probably shouldn't...

There's one thing I know and will never question...

Bleh! It tastes like cardboard.

Despite how hard it is...

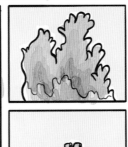

No more board games.

That was awesome!

Moral of the story is take a flask to everything!

NO IT'S NOT!

No. Really. No. The moral is to not take weird gifts from strangers!

End.

OUR PARENTS MUST HAVE TOLD US DOZENS OF TIMES NOT TO GO INTO THE DEEP WOODS.

BUT SINCE THAT FATEFUL AFTERNOON, THEIR WARNINGS HAVE REPLAYED IN MY HEAD COUNTLESS TIMES A DAY.

The Last Tea Party

by Sarah O'Donnell

THEY DIDN'T WANT US TO LOSE OUR MOTHER'S PRIZED TEA CUPS.

BACK THEN, THEIR WORDS WERE SO EASILY FORGOTTEN.

AND SO,

MY SISTER WAS TAKEN,

KRAK

AND, LESS IMPORTANTLY, SO WAS MY LIFE.

28

NO. WHAT? MOOSEY, YOU REALLY THINK THAT'S WHAT A CUPCAKE LOOKS LIKE?

I SOWWEE, SIR OWWA. I TWY.

CUPCAKES HAVE, LIKE... STUFF ON TOP! YOU'RE JUST MAKING DIRT BALLS.

AND IT'S PRONOUNCED "OH-LAH." MY NAME IS OLA.

YEARS AGO, I'VE TAKEN UP ARMS TO DEFEND THIS FOREST AGAINST THE WOLVES THAT CLAIMED MY SISTER AND MY LIFE.

I GUESS WE COULD PRETEND THEY'RE TRUFFLES.

I TWY AGAIN.

HOW THEY FOUND ME STILL REMAINS A PUZZLE. BUT THEY CLEANED ME UP AND TOOK ME IN. THEY GAVE ME HUMAN SIZED ARMOR THAT THEY SAID WAS ENCHANTED BY FAIRIES FROM LONG AGO.

IN EXCHANGE, I SWORE ALLEGIANCE TO THEIR MYSTERIOUS KINGDOM HIDDEN WITHIN THESE WOODS.

I AM, FOR ALL INTENTS AND PURPOSES, A GHOUL THAT LIVES IN A FOREST.

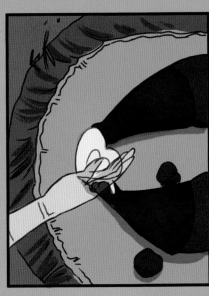

BUT THIS KINGDOM I SERVE HAS MADE ME RETHINK WHAT MY LIMITATIONS TRULY ARE.

YOU READY, POGO? TEA TIME.

POGO!?

SHE GONE.

WHAT!? NOT AGAIN!

POOOOO GOOOOO! OH MY GOD

SLAM!

MOOSEY.

YUP.

YOU'RE **CAUSING** A SCENE.

SWOOSH

POGO! POGO!? WHERE ARE YOU?!

WHY SHE DO THIS THING.

BECAUSE SHE'S LITERALLY SO ANNOYING THAT OUR OWN KING AND QUEEN WANTED HER OUT.

WHEN'S FOOD GONNA BE READY? I'M A GUEST HERE YANNOW! I'M COOOOLD.

TRIPLE YOUR PAY. HER ESCORT WAS MISTAKENLY EATEN BY OUR PRIEST.

YOU PAY ME IN FOOD I COULD NOT EAT WERE I STILL ALIVE.

PLEASE DO THIS. YOU ARE MUCH TALLER THAN WE ARE.

UGH. FINE.

AND, UH, TAKE MOOSEY WITH YOU.

THE PORCUPINE THAT'S NAMED AFTER A MOOSE AND TALKS LIKE A LITERAL BABY?

HE'S YOUR SQUIRE NOW.

DOUBLE UGH.

DOUBLE UGH.

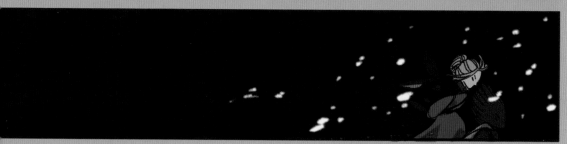

DERE BE
WOLVES.

NO--

fwsh

HO. A HUMAN GIRL.

Y-YOU CAN SEE ME?

YOUR ARMOR IS ENCHANTED, NO? IN THE SAME WAY YOU CAN PICK UP YOUR SWORD, YOU CAN UNDERSTAND MY WORDS.

I CAN SEE WHAT THE WOLVES SEE. I COMMUNICATE THE WAY THEY DO.

I, TOO, AM A HUMAN KNIGHT ORDAINED TO PROTECT WOODLAND CREATURES.

IS THIS.. YOURS?

YA HANDS ARE SO COLD. GAWSH.

...

I AM DUTY-BOUND TO SEE THAT ANIMAL RETURNS HOME SAFELY.

37

The End

Goldie and The Witch of the Woods
by Megan Brennan

Maybe the elders made some kind of mistake...

Maybe when I meet the witch she'll say it was all a mix-up, and she'll just let me go home instead of finding a cursed object and being killed in an epic battle or whatever fate has in store for me!

Plink
Plink

But then I'll have borrowed and worn all this heavy armor for no reason...

SIGH.

"Find The Witch of the Woods in the house at the edge of the forest"

Okay.

Well.

GULP

KNOCK
KNOCK!
KNOCK!

CREAAAK!

What if this witch gets me killed and THEN uses necromancy to bring me BACK, and it's even WORSE than if I just stayed dead in the first place.

Here it is, in the heart of the forest.

An egg?

Not just an egg, it's a PHOENIX egg.

The goblin elders said you knew the old, powerful songs. Just play them near the egg and everything will work out.

Why am I supposed to play music for an EGG? What are you even going to DO with a phoenix?

A phoenix chick needs music to know know when it's safe to hatch. This is one of the last Phoenix eggs left...

I will raise it to be strong and powerful! I'll astonish all those nitwits on the witch's council! As if my rivals could EVER do something more impressive than THIS!

ALISON
KNIGHT of WANDS.

LISA
KNIGHT of SWORDS

I don't think
I'm strong enough...

But I have to try...

BLAZING

ANGEL!!

The End

"THE RULES"

STORY AND ART:
JD BENEFIELD

THE FIRST *RULE* ABOUT BEING A KNIGHT, HILD: *ALWAYS FULFILL YOUR OATH.*

BUT, CYNEBURG, I WAS *DRUNK* AT THE TIME...

DOESN'T MATTER. AN *OATH* IS STILL AN *OATH.*

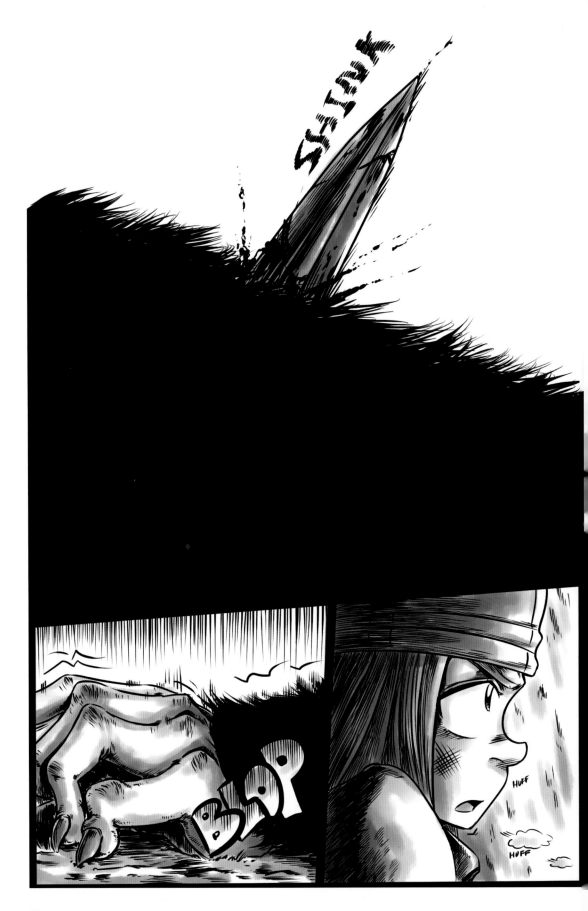

BY THROWING THEM DOWN A HILL?
IT GOT YA DOWN QUICK, DIDN'T IT?
UGH...
LET'S JUST GET OUT OF HERE.
GOOD IDEA! THERE'S AN ALE-HOUSE NEARBY, TOO!
LET'S... NOT.
PHOOEY!
STILL, DESPITE YER GRIPING, I'M PROUD OF YA.
YA DID GOOD, HILD.
UH... THANKS.
M-MAYBE I'LL HAVE ONE DRINK.
NOW THAT'S WHAT I WANT TO HEAR!
END!

The Hunter and the Swan

by C. S. Hunsher

CAMPGROU

LAKE

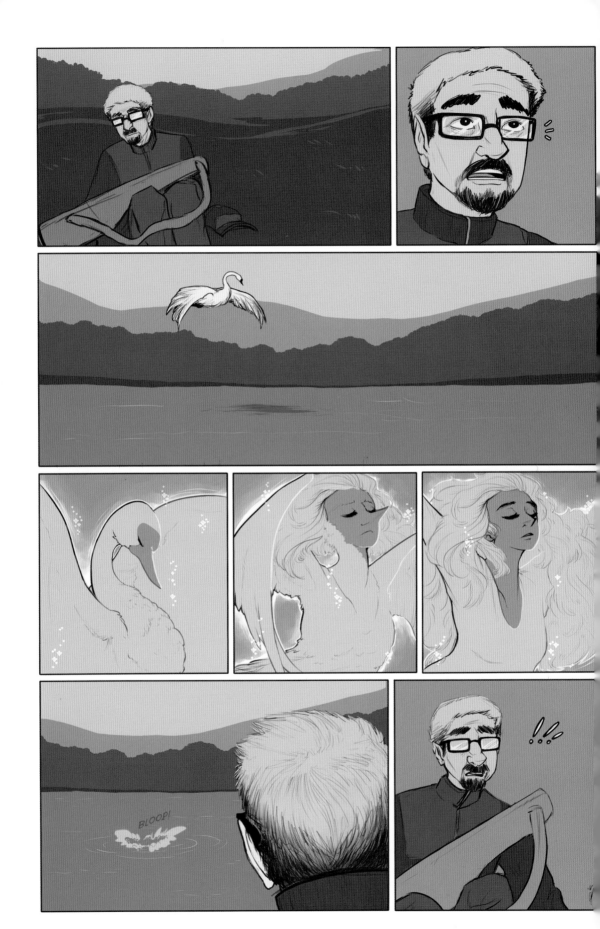

BLOOP!

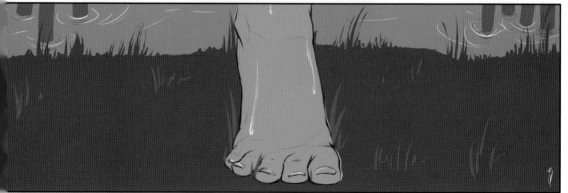

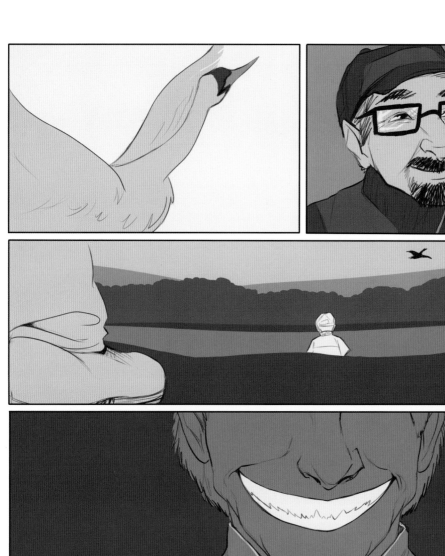

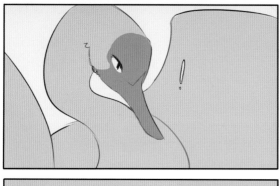

FIN.

BENEATH YOUR NOTICE

WE FIGHT SO HARD TO SURVIVE

BLANKET FORT KNIGHTS
JESS HURLEY

THWACK

WE DID IT! WE'VE DEFENDED THE KINGDOM AGAIN!

IT'S SAFE BECAUSE OF US!

AWESOME!

WOO!

She risked much to bring our pack to safety.

And as the war dragged on, she brought more of us to that old supply room.

There were so many of us. She did not always know what to do.

But when we started to *change*, she taught us to be human.

And when we got a bit *older*...

...she taught us to be *knights.*

The memories started to teach us again.

I remember the rasping voice.

Chico remembers the cold eyes.

Alia remembers the smell of fear.

No.

The smell of death.

Nwain:
The Knight Who
Wandered Dream

O' King Noonwright,
What have you built for me?
One great loom of light,
Warm and fire-free.

O' dear king of mine,
What have you spun for me?
One vast knot in time,
A yearful tapestry.

O' Gnomon King,
My mask agleam with dew,
I ask the wind and sea,
What would I give for you?

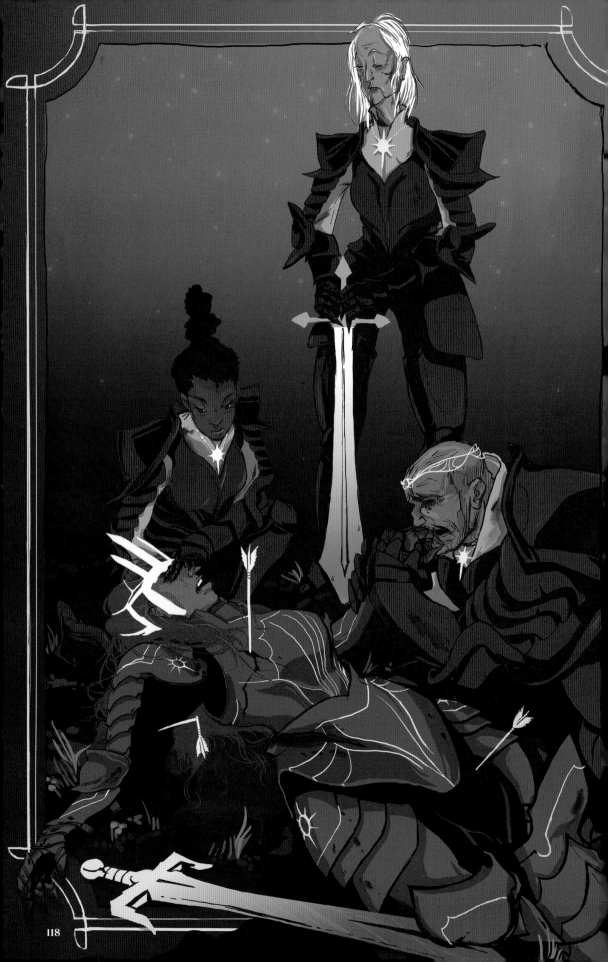

The Great Eeldragons of Pen
by Rachel Kahn

Sir Halbrig
The Relentless

Dame Trapp
The Thorn

Sir Moonscale
The Fishing Knight

Sir Leopold
The Twice Turned

DIRGESINGER ARASYS!!

SO LIKE YOUR KIND, EAGER FOR A STRUGGLE.

CRACKLE!

WHAT CAN YOU DO TO "END" ME WHEN YOUR PREDECESSORS COULDN'T DECADE AFTER DECADE? THEY GOT CLOSE, OH, THEY DID.

CRACKLE!

BUT I CAN'T DIE. I REFUSE TO DIE. THE DEAD DANCE AND THE GRAND GUIGNOL MUST GO ON, MY LADY CAPTAIN!

I'VE COME TOO FAR TO JUST STOP!

WHY?

GLEAM!

SWISH!

SCHWING!

SO COOL!

WHAT... WHAT DO YOU MEAN "WHY"?

DECADES IS A LONG TIME TO BE MAKING SKELETONS AND ZOMBIES.

SO YEAH, YOU KNOW, WHY? WHY NOT STOP?

IS THIS ALL YOU REALLY WANT ARASYS?

WHAT I REALLY WANT... OF COURSE, IT IS, I ...

THE END

PROLOGUE
BY SOFIA NEHLAWI

The cave is damp, moldy, forgotten by time. Nore can hardly believe that anything lives down in the darkness. It's just another hole in the mountainside, one of many. She's sure that she's gotten the directions from someone reputable (or somewhat so) in the last city before heading out for the mountain range. There aren't many people who know where the Crone lives, and even less know if she's still alive anymore. But Nore knows she has to try. It's her very last option, the only name left on the list.

Carefully, Nore steps into the maw of the mountainside, peering into the pitch darkness. She half expects the ground to be flattened, the path clear and easy to walk. People know about the Crone, know what she can do. Why aren't there more people here to see her? Why isn't the road into her den prominent to all? Nore at least expects some kind of sign, some way to positively know that this is the right way, that she won't walk into the heart of the Cobalt Mountains, through them, and appear on the other side without ever having run into the Crone.

"Faith," they had cautioned her. "Even if you don't believe you must pretend to. Convince yourself. If you don't, Cobalt will eat you, freeze you, turn you blue and brittle."

She had scoffed. Superstitions. Rumors. In her country, baseless whisperings like those were stamped out, the sources silenced. They didn't tolerate those things.

But this is not her country, and reminding herself to keep an open mind takes its toll, even with a merchant like herself. Who was to say that the power of faith didn't do strange things when relied upon?

She leaves her caution behind and starts her descent into the mountain's belly, keeping one hand on the wall. She tries not to think that she is leaving the world behind, fresh air and people and the ability to turn back when she realizes how fruitless the whole journey is. No one can bring back a dead person. No one can retrieve the soul. No one can and no one will. It's a simple fact of life that Nore knows well.

And yet she still hopes, still clings to the vision that her Laurel will come back and hold her hand and smile, bathe her in warmth. She still hopes when she knows she shouldn't, that it's wrong to wish.

The silence presses in all around Nore as she continues, careful not to trip over loose stones and sharp rocks. The bundle on her shoulder, her precious cargo, jostles slightly with every step, the weight pushing her more and more into the ground as she walks. She's careful to make sure that it doesn't hit the walls, that the head doesn't scrape the ceiling. The body must stay perfect, just the way it was when Laurel died. It wouldn't do to bring her back into a bruised body. If she can be brought back at all.

Nore is already sweating heavily when she reaches the first chamber. She feels the way the path before her opens up, the echoing of her steps, the wall under her fingertips that drops away. A pocket in the mountain, one of probably thousands. She can't see, even though her eyes have long since adjusted to the darkness. She puts down her Laurel and bag, fumbling in the darkness at her waist for the lantern. She yanks it off her belt, digs out the box of matches from her pocket, and feels out a match with steady fingers before striking it on the side of the box. Fire blooms like a flower in the cave, and Nore works fast, opening the lantern and lighting the wick inside before blowing out the match. The lantern casts her shadow on the walls, exaggerated and misshapen. But they start to glitter as her lantern flickers in the darkness, shiny onyx and mica.

It's also empty. Nore clicks her tongue, brow furrowed deeply, and shoulders her load again before immediately heading into the darkness on the other side of the room. Her footsteps are the only sounds in the cavern.

She walks. She has no idea for how long or for how far. The Cobalt Mountains must be deep and vast, must descend through the heart of the world and spit you out on the other side. That must be the only reason that Nore feels like she's been walking for years, for half of her life. She feels the hunger in her belly, the cinderblock weight of her love, the steady throb in her mind. Does she have a mind anymore? That's a good question, but one she cannot dare entertain. She's sure that if she thinks, if she considers what she's doing, then she'll stop moving, just collapse where she is, and finally, blissfully, die. Die without ever finishing what she set out to do in the first place.

She'll be damned if she lets that happen.

And then she's suddenly...there. The tunnel opens up again into another cavern, but this one is enormous compared to the last. Nore's eyes strain as she lifts the lantern slightly, trying to see the other side of the room. But she can't. The meager light only brightens up a small half-circle around her. It slides over the edge of something and it's only when she walks closer to it that she realizes that she's not alone in the room, that there's something breathing the same air as her. Something alive and old. She knows it's there, that it's the Crone, knows that she has reached the end of her journey. She doesn't have to walk anymore. She doesn't have to drag herself deeper into cities and deserts and her own mind anymore. She doesn't have to keep carrying anymore, keep up the mask of strength.

"Sit." The Crone's voice scratches, breath rattling in her chest. Nore nods, dropping her pack and oversized bundle before sitting on the ground on the other side of the dais from the Crone, a respectful distance. She places the lantern in front of her on the dais, hoping that it'll illuminate even a fraction of her companion. But it only makes the shadows longer, deeper. They shiver and leap and laugh on the jagged walls.

She can't see what the Crone looks like, not unless she scoots forward and unwraps the cloth that covers every inch of her. But Nore can tell that she is small, maybe half her size, if that were possible. And the hands that lie loosely folded in her lap are thin, so thin and brittle, even in the twilight gloom of the cave. Nore half thinks that she'll dissolve then and there, turn to dust. She looks like just taking another breath, just moving, will cause her to fall apart.

But the Crone does it anyway. The huddle of limbs inhales, a wheezing, rattling breath, and Nore waits patiently until she's sure the Crone won't speak again before finally saying her piece, what she has traveled all this way, across unknown countries and silent forests and petrified oceans to know, to do. She'll say her wish, and if it's impossible, then she'll finally go home, keep her promise, settle down and find peace. She would live the rest of her life for the both of them.

But only if.

"You bring dead people back to life." Nothing, the silence wrapping snugly around them, pressing down on Nore's shoulders, her brow. She wipes the sweat from her upper lip, suddenly hot, the room stifling, before barreling on. "I need you to do this for me."

"You're not dead." Does she imagine it, or is there something like amusement in the clattering voice?

"I know." Nore leans forward, eager to explain herself, launch into her story of leaving her family farm behind to be a merchant in the closest city, of tripping over her words at the sight of a paladin with her helmet off, of settling down in the city to see the paladin more, of letting her hand go one day and welcoming a body back, bloodied and bruised. Of knowing love and losing it.

But the Crone's hand holds back the onslaught of Nore's words, and she bites her lip, trying to calm down. She feels herself shaking, hands clenched on her knees, almost overwhelmed with her feelings. But she can't falter now. She must be clear and direct. She must be honest. She must have faith.

"Your knight is dead."

"Yes." Nore's eyes flicker to the body beside her, the one she's been carrying this whole time, for days, days she's lost count. She hasn't looked at her Laurel since she left, wrapping her body carefully, securing her on Nore's shoulder so she wouldn't be so heavy. Nore's sure she's been decomposing all this time, and no amount of strange smelling herbal potions and blessed waters and prayers has held back the stench. She's never unwrapped the body.

"You want her alive." Nore remembers Laurel taking her hand, guiding her fingers to her horse, carefully resting her trembling hand on the beast's head and letting her pet slowly, gently.

'She's a sweetie,' she had laughed, her voice low and solid. 'She loves pets.'

Nore swallows, staring at the Crone's hood, where her head must be. She nods.

"Put her there." One of the hands rises, pointing to the dais. Nore scrambles up, picking up Laurel (no, not Laurel anymore but soon she will be again) and placing her in the middle of the dais. It's only when she's kneeling that Nore notices that the platform feels smooth and polished, but doesn't glitter like the walls do. It feels like one big piece of glass.

It also feels warm.

"Stay there." The Crone mumbles, command loud in the dark, and Nore feels herself immobilized by those words. She hears rustling from where the Crone is and her heart leaps into her throat. Her hands shake. Fear strikes her fast and deep, resting in her chest and contracting around her heart. She is suddenly very aware that she is alone, completely alone, with this woman - no - this thing, and she's asked it for a favor.

But Nore doesn't move, doesn't flee. Running means leaving Laurel, leaving her gorgeous knight, her glittering armor and shy smile and sturdy hands that swing a spear and hold her hand tightly. She cannot run. She has run the whole way here. She cannot run back.

"You came here to offer anything to me right?" The Crone's voice is right in front of her, and Nore looks up to see the cloak half covering Laurel, now partially revealed. Nore knows she can see her face, if she looked. But she doesn't. She keeps her eyes on the darkness of the Crone's hood, at the nothingness she sees in there. How can she not see her face if she's so close?

"Yes." Her voice cracks, echoes. The light flickers, dipping lower. It's almost out.

"Do one thing for me and I'll bring her to you."

The words are more than Nore could ever hope for, could ever have dreamed of. She gasps aloud, one hand covering her mouth as she nods furiously. She never imagined that the Crone would be here, much less help her. But what she has traveled so far for, for so long, she finally has.

"Yes!" She shouts, voice reverberating in the cave. "Anything! Name your one thing!"

The world is still. The light stops dancing, the shadows motionless.
Nothing breathes.

And then everything explodes.

Pain rises into a crescendo in Nore's chest, and a scream tears its way out from between her clenched teeth. She never saw the movement, but now her eyes catch up, her senses ignite. The pain in her chest is shooting up faster and faster, climbing in her mind and pressing against her lungs and the backs of her eyes, banging around the inside of her skull. She knows her body is trying desperately to repair the damage, keep her up and going. But as each second passes, her breath gets more and more labored, her limbs get tired. And still, what happened?

"Ahhh." The Crone breathes, taking out her hand from Nore's chest. The merchant's vision is getting fuzzy; she feels impossibly warm, burning, aflame. But she can see how grossly wet the Crone's hand looks, how she slowly spreads it up her arm.

How the skin vanishes.

"It's just enough." She croaks, hooded head bobbing slightly, a nod. Nore feels her body collapse on Laurel's long-since lifeless one. But it doesn't feel like her body anymore. It feels like she's floating out to sea and she left her body back on the beach.

"I just needed a little more before I could finally disappear. I thank you." The Crone laughs, a sound like loose teeth on cobblestones, like a door opening in a sleeping house, like hail and bitter winds. Nore remembers, in a flash, a forest she passed through on her way here, trees black and dead, silent.

"I will reward you though." The cloak opens, and there's nothing in the air. It should surprise Nore, but her mind is already gray, and she can feel her body shutting down.

"You'll see your dear knight when you wake up again." The Crone, the Voice, speaks from the air, as if passing judgment. "You will see her again and again and again, in all ways, in all manners. You will love her, and you will lose her."

"No." Nore hisses, gritting her teeth.

"Yes. That is the world. You cannot bring the dead back to life. You can only keep living." She pauses. "The life you both find peace in is the last one you'll have together."

And then the room is empty, the cloak drops. Nore grabs it desperately, feeling nothing but fabric. And then she breathes out, closing her eyes.

At least she's with Laurel. At least they are together.

The lantern flickers one last time before going out.

WE ARE AT WAR.

WE LIVE IN A TIME WHERE OUR ENEMIES AWAIT OUR EVERY MOVE.

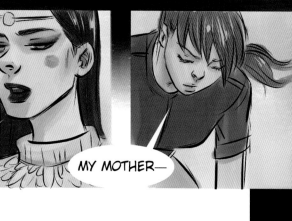

AAAH!

WHOOOOSH

KSST

K

THESE OTHER WOMEN...THEY WERE ONCE OUR NEIGHBORS.

YET THEIR HUNGER OUTGREW OUR PEACE.

153

OUR NUMBERS ARE SMALL, BUT WE ARE THE BEST. WE MUST PREVAIL.

WELL DONE, JASMINE.

THANK YOU, MY EMPRESS.

IT IS ONE OF MANY, WE HAVE FAR TO GO.

SINCE YOU'VE TAKEN OVER, THE TIDE HAS BEEN TURNING.

DON'T DOUBT YOURSELF AGAIN.

COME, MY PRINCE. LET'S WELCOME THESE MEN HOME.

ONCE I'M DONE SAVING OUR PEOPLE,
I WILL FREE YOU, TOO.

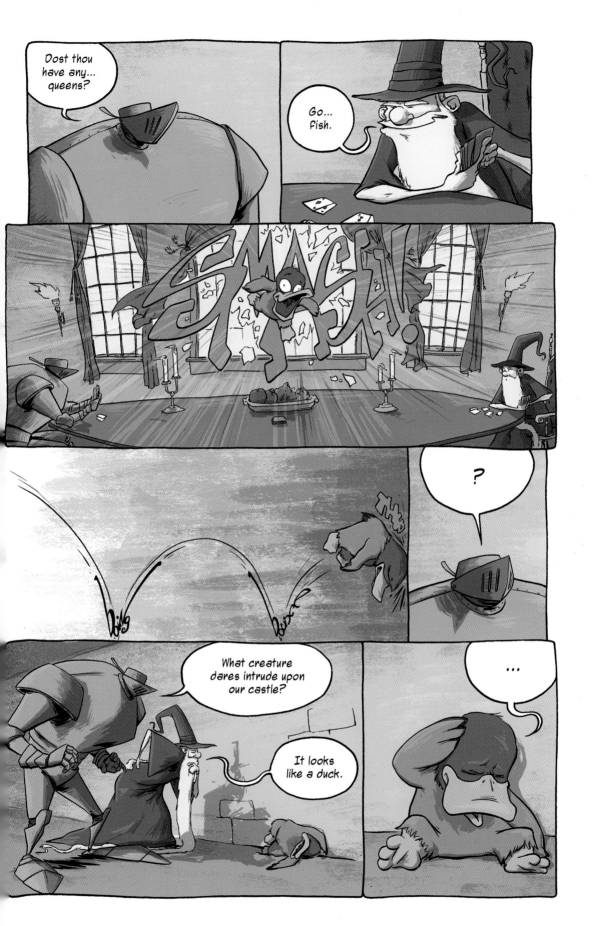

POWERS
BY SOFIA NEHLAWI

The Light jumps from rooftop to rooftop, making sure her footing is light and sure. Yes, she's rushing. Yes, the sooner she gets home, the sooner she can pretend like she was there the whole time when the news comes on. She's sure her mother will give her The Look, asking without actually asking if it's all her fault, if she started it again. Yes, it is her fault. But Liara isn't about to come clean to it. Not to her mother and not to the Powered Police.

Definitely not to the Powered Police. They'd just end up finally arresting her and tossing her in with all those other poor people with genetic abnormalities. People who could regrow lost limbs and turn into smoke and breathe fire hot enough to melt metal, fire straight from their stomach. People that turned up in schools or their jobs, somehow losing control during an ordinary day. People that no one saw again after their little outburst of power.

It's a government thing, everyone knows that. They take care of everything, them and the Powered Police, equipped with tranquilizers and sedatives and bullets strong enough to punch through three feet of concrete and dissolve all kinds of mental barriers that a Powered had.

She would know. She had seen it firsthand when they had taken in Sovereign.

Another leap, and she just barely manages to get both feet on the roof. Her prize, the data on a flashdrive, is safe in her pocket. Liara's thankful that she's not the kind of thief that takes crazy expensive things, things that they always show in movies: jewels, gold bars, stacks of cash.

That stuff is nice. But info, that's where real power lies. If you have information, everything else comes.

The sirens are still far off, but as soon as they find out exactly how she got into the building, they're bound to send in a Powered squad, stomping boots and black lines in red Kevlar suits. The suits themselves were shit against most Powered. But people got out of their way and that was all that mattered: intimidation.

Liara makes her way out of the heart of the city, carefully placing her jumps, timing them so she catches as few eyes as possible. Quick. Quiet. It doesn't need to be perfect, just right. Every second that passes means they're catching up, that they're figuring things out. They'll get a psychic out to chase her down if they can rouse one out of heavy sedation. But if not, they'll just throw as many Police at her, in all directions, and then that'll be the end.

She can't let that happen. She won't.

It happens when she touches down on one of the taller corporate buildings. They're in their own sector, away from most of the government structures, and Liara thinks it's the best place for her to pause, if only for a moment, and take a quick breather. As great as her powers are, they take a lot of energy out of her. Great powers come with great consequences blah blah blah.

She holds her side, resting one foot on the ledge as she stares in the direction of the Spire, the main government building. She can hear the sirens now, but the distance and general noise of traffic soften them slightly. They're probably frantic now, sending desperate calls out to all the other connected facilities. They probably took all the files and tech off the main grid too. It'll be wiped in less than a day, and they'll have to make a new one from scratch, tighten the doors and windows.

The thought brings a grim smile to The Light's face. They should scramble. They should be scared. Now they'll feel what she's felt her whole life, what people like her have been feeling since kids that displayed psychic powers went missing in the night. Since all known people with powers had trackers implanted into their shoulders. Since her father took three in the back when she was a kid to protect her from the Police after she let her bike float into the atmosphere by accident. They should be afraid.

"Stop!" Is the shout from the other side of the roof, and Liara freezes, every nerve in her body petrified. She made sure to take a different path this night. The information she has is so sensitive it could break open everything in their metropolis, in their world. She had made sure to tell no one, to plan out different routes in case something happened, to time herself. It was all supposed to go according to plan, her plan! So why is it suddenly spinning out of control!? "Raise your hands!"

She does, slowly. She knows these officers: one movement that's too quick, too sudden, and they start shooting until you're full of holes. Hell, half of them don't even wait for you to listen to them, just shoot you down anyway and say you tried to set them on fire or something ridiculous like that. But, as her hands finally go up, as she turns slightly, Liara knows who's there.

"Heeeey it's Nims!" She winks, like she's planned this whole meeting. Her heart keeps on thudding away in her chest, not fooled.

Neither is Nima. "It's Nima to you." She pauses, eyes narrowing more, lips pursing. "Scratch that. It's Officer Gadhavi. I know what you're doing."

"You do?" Liara does her best to sound surprised. "That's pretty amazing. Even I don't know what I'm up to."

"Don't give me that garbage." Nima growls, gun still up. "Why else are the alarms going off? Why else am I getting radio noise about something The Light stole?" She motions to Liara with the muzzle of her gun. "You did something tonight and I'm going to take you in."

The Light pauses, watching the officer from behind her mask. If this were any other time, she would lie. She would lie through her teeth until there was even the smallest opening for her to get away, and tease her a little more before darting off, quick like the wind. She would talk circles around Nima until her head spun. Hell, she'd done it before. It is the very reason Nima still doesn't trust her.

The flashdrive is sitting in her pocket, burning a hole through the fabric, and still, she wants to stay here and mess around. She wants to bounce on the rooftop with the officer and goof off and tell her stupid stuff. She wants to waste time when she should be getting away, getting to her little safe house to hand off the info.

Why? Why does she want to stay with Nima so badly?

And then it clicks. It's like clouds separating to reveal the sun.

She's seen her before, met her. She's known Nima, somehow. Not physically, not in the flesh. But in some other, ethereal way. Like as Liara but not Liara.

"You know, I dreamed about you." The Light pinwheels her arms as she walks along the ledge, peering down to look at the city streets every now and then. Every step, every little lean makes Nima shift slightly, like she's ready to leap forward and grab Liara if she tumbles over the edge. A smirk quirks the corners of Liara's lips.

"Really?" The sarcasm is heavy in the officer's voice.

"I did!" The Light stops, turning on her heel to finally face the Powered officer. She has to have her believe, has to know if Nima is dreaming the same things she is. "I dreamed we were together! And that you had a sword and made me laugh and that we were happy."

"I'm flattered."

"No you don't get it!" Liara stomps her foot, pouting. "The dream was real. It happened. Maybe not now, but at some other time. It means something! It means that there's a reason why you're always so close behind me all the time and why I always stick around to mess with you. It has a real message, a real meaning. It's real!"

She pauses, trying to catch her breath. Nima is standing so still, face serious. But she lowers the gun slightly, even as she shakes her head. "That makes no sense."

"But-"

"That's all it is: a dream." She sounds like she's trying to convince herself more than Liara, her eyes down.

"So how did you find me then?"

"What?" Nima spits the confusion like acid, like she's eaten something spoiled. "What's that supposed to mean?"

"If you didn't know what I was going to do tonight or where I would be, how did you get here before I did?"

Nima's mask breaks for a second, and Liara sees all of it. She sees the horror, the confusion, the fury. She sees the late nights written into the lines in her forehead and between her eyebrows. She sees the reoccurring dreams, the ones that feel so familiar yet so distant, play out in Nima's mind. Liara can see it all, not because she's psychic (they would've carted her sorry ass off a long time ago if they knew), but because she's had them all already. She's had them since she was five, every night, every month, every year, up until this moment. And she's been able to guess what the officer hasn't.

And then mask is back, and Liara knows she'll never get through to her. She can give her all the proof she needs, tell her all the dreams she's had that she knows Nima's been having too. And still, the Powered officer will say that Liara read her mind, that she used her powers to manipulate her, that she did something to somehow know what Nima's never told anyone.

"You're just a Powered trying to catch me off guard!" The gun is back up again, pointed straight at Liara's face. Liara recoils, heel off the ledge. "You're probably a psychic. You're probably poking around in my head right now!"

"No, I-"

"This is exactly why I joined the force! To protect people from Powered like you!"

"Listen to me!"

"Powered who just try to manipulate others to get what they want! Powered who hurt the people who can't defend themselves!"

"We're the ones who can't defend ourselves!" Liara howls, throwing her head back, and the building rumbles under her feet, threatening to pull free from its foundation. How dare she, how dare she!

"We're the ones going missing, turning up dead after weeks! We're the ones you should be protecting! You don't get to pick and choose who needs help and who doesn't! You're not a good person by choosing who to save and who to kill! If you can't even save those kids that always go missing on the news then what good are you!? What kind of sorry white-knight are you if you can't even find us, help us?! You should protect everyone, not just the people who pay you! You should protect us too!"

Liara stops, panting, empty and shaking. Her hands are balled into fists and she can't remember when that happened. She's all out of words and patience and tries and why doesn't she understand? Why doesn't she see? In her dreams, Nima (not Nima but she doesn't know what else to call her) always gets her, always soothes her. But that's not happening here.

"Light...." Nima lowers the gun, and Liara can see the confusion plain on her face, the pain of not knowing.

"Forget it." The vigilante waves her hands, shaking her head. She faces Nima, back to the city as she stares at the officer, letting a smile creep across her face. "Maybe one day it'll work out. I'd like to know what you dream about."

Nima is at a loss, staring at The Light. So she just nods slowly, and The Light nods back. "I'll see you around Nims."

And then she falls backwards off the roof.

"Fuck!" Nima shouts, running to the edge of the building. Even from this high up, she'll hear the screams, see the frantic people running from a body.

But there's no one, just the street far below, cars like ants on their way back to their homes.

She hears the clatter next to her, notices the white mask at her feet. And as she picks it up, she remembers last night's dream. She remembers holding someone's hand and hearing them laughing and thinking that there's such a thing as peace.

A voice crackles from the officer's radio, and she hooks the earpiece over her ear, speaking into the mic.

"Did you get her?!" Shouts in the background, angry yelling.

You should protect everyone, not just the people who pay you! You should protect us too!

"Nope." Nima sighs, holstering her gun. She holds the mask tightly in her hand, thumb rubbing the white leather. "She got away."

BERNICE

CLASS HERALD

LVL 14   XP 380K

ALN LAWFUL GOOD   LCK 15

STR
CON
DEX
INT
WIS
CHR

+1   —
-1   —
+5   +5

PAUL.REINWAND

Zha

CLASS *thaumaturgy*

LVL 16   XP 790k

ALN *chaotic good*   LCK 10

STR
CON
DEX
INT
WIS
CHR

+7   +7
+7   -1
-3   -

STR
CON
DEX
INT
WIS
CHR

Niss
CLASS physiker
LVL 12   XP 156k
ALN neutral   LCK 13
    evil

+5   +5
+5   +5
+5   +5

KILRIC

CLASS BRUISER

LVL 15   XP 550 K

ALN NEUTRAL LCK 8

STR
CON
DEX
INT
WIS
CHR

✧ —   ◊ +5
✧ —   ✧ +5
◊ +5   ✧ -10

PAUL.REINWAND

Two adventurers (met by chance), two lovers became in time
They adventured much and more, until captured and torn apart!
But they fought and broke their chains, reunited once again
and they vowed to stay together, never far, a bond unbroken
never to be again apart, never to break the vow they'd spoken

179

Daniel Shaffer

Showtimes

Market......10-4
Castle......11-3
Petting Zoo...12-3
History......10
Puppets......12
Joust........2
Closing......4

Info

IT'S THE

POST GUARD

BY REL

—CAN STAY THESE COURIERS FROM THEIR APPOINTED COURSE OF DUTY!

WE'RE THE POST GUARD, WE ARE.

WE GET THE MAIL *DELIVERED*.

HERE'S YOUR PACKAGE!

OH, THANK YOU!

MENDING
BY CAREY PIETSCH

YOU THINK THEY REALLY USE COMET ALLOYS IN ALL THEIR BUCKLES?

CAN WE GET A CLOSER LOOK?

ARE YOU SERIOUS?!

DID YOU *HEAR* WHAT THEY SAID ABOUT US?

THEY'D NEVER LET—

BREE!!

UH.

IT'S HURT*!!*

DO YOU WANNA END UP AS A DRAGON SNACK?!

THEY'LL *FIX* IT *LATER!*

MAYBE,

BUT IT'S HURT *NOW*.

YOU ARE GONNA BE THE DEATH OF US.

IF YOU GET STUCK HALFWAY UP, ANYWAY.

COME ON!

SQUELCH

OH.

YOU DON'T... REALLY EAT PEOPLE...

...DO YOU?

THERE! ALL BETTER!

SEE, I TOLD YOU—

HELLO.

AND WHAT BRINGS YOU HERE?

UM.

WELL,

WE LET HER IN!!

199

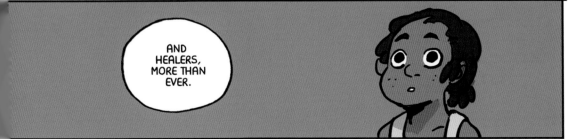

WHEN YOU'RE ALL OLD ENOUGH TO JOIN A TRADE,

SEND A MESSAGE MY WAY.

BUT AH— FOR NOW, MAYBE YOU'D BEST CLEAR OUT BEFORE SOMEONE ELSE COMES AFTER ME?

THANKS LET'S GO LET'S GO LET'S GOOO

PROPHECY
BY SOFIA NEHLAWI

hameless," The bodyguard mutters as the huge gilt doors groan and close behind her. She's told them a thousand times that it'll be a pain in the ass to pull them back open again. But they always insist that the Prophet needs privacy. Their problem. She doesn't care if their backs give out early from all that door-pulling.

"I have no idea what you're talking about." A voice mutters from the other side of the room. She can clearly imagine the Prophet's terrible bedhead, and how much trouble it'll be to brush it before the ceremony. She'll probably end up punching one of the attendants in the mouth again. "I've only been sleeping."

The bodyguard strides across the room, following the clear path around new stacks of baubles and books and expensive furniture from worshippers. It's a good thing that the Prophet's attendants organized everything yesterday; she wasn't sure she would be able to stand another day of hopping over things and having to backtrack and find another path because everything was so impossibly heaped together like a maze. A very colorful, glittering, expensive maze, filled with little glass orbs suspended from the ceiling with flowers floating in them, statues in the Prophet's likeness, and chests of clothes and jewelry and books of all kinds, from all corners of the globe. It was truly a maze, and the bodyguard was always hard-pressed to find her way to the Prophet, and then find her way out.

But today was, thankfully, different. She could see across the room. The statues had all been pushed back to opposite sides, books stacked and shelved in the three bookcases that dominated the left side of the room. She could see the marble floors, the rugs that lay over them (to protect the Prophet's precious feet from the earth), the little knickknacks placed tastefully on side tables. Finally, order.

On the far side of the room, tucked into a corner and sectioned off by stacked dressers and chests, is the Prophet's bed. The bodyguard grabs the corner of the sheet and snaps it off in one quick movement.

"Naia!" Lei sputters as she tries to shield her face and body and legs all at the same time. Naia doesn't bat an eye at the shriek, only begins folding the blanket. "I still have time! They don't need me out there until—"

"Midmorning, which will be the time in another half hour." Naia places the blanket on the edge of the bed and sits in one of the gilt chairs. "You don't have long to get ready."

"Shit!" The Prophet jumps up, stumbling over discarded clothes and books and jewelry as she makes her way to one of the trunks. She kneels, furiously pulling out robe after robe, throwing each one over her shoulder. Her attendants hurry into the room from one of the smaller side doors and start helping her, pulling out clothing and tugging her up so they can dress her. The whole thing is a little like a performance, and Naia finds herself watching them, fascinated, before Lei snaps her out of her daze. "How hot it is outside?"

"Blistering." The bodyguard sighs, gesturing to her sleeveless tunic and loose pants. "I didn't even attempt sandals today."

"Then I won't either." The Prophet stops any disagreement from her helpers with a wave of her hand. They finish wrapping her in her clothes in record time, cool blue and green layers of silk, perfect to soothe the eyes of the populace. Smart choices; the people will feel the heat today, be extra thirsty during their time with the Prophet. She must be like an oasis in the desert to them, and now she looks it.

Lei goes over to Naia and plops down in front of her on the floor, back to her, and it takes a moment before the bodyguards gets it. "I'll do your hair?"

"Of course." Lei laughs, ignoring the way her attendants twitter, unhappy to have such a short time with the Prophet. Naia grabs the brush on the table nearby and starts untangling the black locks before her, letting Lei's words wash over her like water. "My tireless guardian always brushes my hair best."

"Ah, do I?"

"Yes! But first: did you know that I dreamed about you again last night?"

Naia's hands slow for a fraction of a second. Her frown deepens slightly. "Oh really? I'm sure I had a small part."

"Not so! We were lovers! You were smiling a lot and you held my hand so tightly! I don't think you frowned once in my whole dream!" She pauses, closing her eyes, probably trying to recall any other details. "You looked a little different: your hair was shorter and your back wasn't as straight all the time. But you were still firm and blunt." She grins, looking over her shoulder at Naia. "You were still you."

"I didn't think I would change even in a dream."

"Do you dream about me too?" The question is an innocent one, but it immediately weighs Naia down. She's dreamed countless dreams of the Prophet, seen her in countless lifetimes and moments and seconds. She's known her more so in dreams then in the waking world.

But the attendants are still in the room, and as Naia starts braiding Lei's hair, she catches the eye of one and scowls, chasing her attention away. There will be rumors later, stories.

Rumors spread fast, even the baseless ones. She's heard them all: stories of the people she's probably killed, how she seduced her way into becoming the Prophet's right hand, how she probably seduces her way into the Prophet's bedchambers at night. The list goes on and on. She's heard them all before: in the dark corridors on her way back from training, when she eats meals with the other soldiers, behind the golden-manicured, jeweled hands of the noblemen and women. They all believe she's somehow enchanted her way into the Prophet's favor. But they're wrong.

"That's my secret Prophet."

She straightens up as she finally finishes braiding Lei's hair, making sure the braid hangs over her shoulder. It's important for the Prophet to imply ease, as well as dignity, to show the people that they could all approach her, but that she is also not one of them, that she is beyond all humans. Still, there's something about a braid that seems almost familiar to Naia. It suits Lei. So whenever the Prophet lets her bodyguard do her hair, Naia always makes a braid.

"How do I look?" Lei stands and twirls, letting Naia take in all her glory, and the bodyguard allows herself a rueful smile.

"Finally ready to do your job."

"You're no fun!" Lei laughs, waving away the rest of the attendants before striding to the door. Naia follows after her, knocking on the door and watching the guards grunt and heave, struggling to open them. Like she said, their problem.

When the doors are finally open, the Prophet bows to the guards in turn, offering them a sweet smile. The effect is instantaneous: the guards beam back, push the doors closed behind her and Naia with minimal sound. It's a skill that Naia has never been able to master no matter how many times she's tried.

When the doors finally close again, the pair set off, heading down the hall towards the main balcony, where the people would already be waiting, arms filled with flowers and gifts, throats filled with songs.

"Do you have any new visions for me? Anything the people should know about?" Lei clings to her bodyguard's arm, doing her best to make her question sound naïve. Naia doesn't pay her any mind, only concentrates on tightening her belt, checking the saber at her waist.

"I already told you all the important stuff: the drought happening in the summer, the food shortage." She pauses, taking the Prophet's arms and disentangling herself from them. "The city will fall in the next twenty years, but you don't need to tell them about that. We'll try to influence the noblemen, the politicians, and get them to take care of that instead." She smiles, patting Lei's hand. "Your job is only to tell the people happy things."

"I can't see why you can't do it." Lei pouts, puffing out her cheeks as she lets bodyguard pull away. She starts off down the hallway again, and Naia falls into step after her, a well-practiced three paces behind the Prophet's stride. "They should be hearing your dreams, hearing how they should protect themselves. Mine are just happy, lame things. They don't even actually happen. They cheer and chant my name. It's your name they should be cheering." She quiets. "You should be living in splendor, not me. I'm just a farce."

"Not true," Naia gently chides, nodding to the guards as they pass the first checkpoint, waiting for the heavy doors before them to open. "The people don't need to hear harsh words all the time. They wouldn't be able to handle truths the way I see them. They would not be able to listen to a rough Prophet. If I were Prophet." She pauses, remembering last night's dream, remembering the barren fields and the dead livestock. She's long since learned that if Lei doesn't appear in her dream, then it'll happen, for sure.

The ones that Lei appears in are ones she doesn't even tell Lei about. Those are too harsh and gruesome for her to speak aloud.

"It feels like we're keeping things from them." The Prophet murmurs, her pout easing slightly as she thinks.

"We are." Naia shrugs as they pass through more doorways, past more guards, nodding to the occasional noble or merchant doing business in the innermost sanctum of the High Chambers, where anybody who has any sort of real power resides. "But we're saving the information for when they can use it best. We can't give the people information before they are ready to hear it. It would wreck them."

"Would it really?"

"Besides, you tell them already. You're forthright with the people: you gently tell them what they should be ready for, how they should continue to stay unified and help each other in their times of need, should they ever arise. They will remember those words when bigger disasters hit, like the famine."

"I suppose you're right." Lei's voice sounds anything but sure, and Naia sighs internally. There's too much honesty in the Prophet, too much goodness. Despite all she's been through, she still believes that that doing the right thing means telling the people everything, even if it's not what they want to hear. Naia's sure that if Lei had it her own way, she would've told them long ago who was really supplying her visions, how the gods smiled no less on her than on any other person.

"Don't worry Prophet." Naia stops them in the middle of the hallway and quickly kneels in front of her, gently taking her hand. There are always times when she needs to remind Lei that she isn't alone, and this seems like one. "I will be at your side every step of the way, and I will continue to provide you with advice, should you need it. It's my duty to protect your mind, as well as your body."

She feels the Prophet still as she kisses the back of her hand, rising from her kneel. She doesn't look her in the face, but as she turns Lei's words stop her, words she's sure she would hear sometime, but not today.

"You love me don't you?"

"As much as the people love you." Naia still doesn't turn. One hand rests idly on the hilt of her saber. "I protect you, and well. So I must care for you in some regard."

"No. I think," Lei hums slightly, and Naia can imagine her mischievous smile, the way she tilts her head. "I think you truly love me."

"Prophet." Naia turns now, careful to keep her face blank as she watches Lei, watches the way her eyes widen and her lips curve up even more, the way she crosses her arms to assert some kind of authority over her bodyguard. "Even if that were true, it can never be." What is she saying? What is she doing, giving herself away so plainly like this? "Gods do not fall in love with humans. They only lead them."

"Hm." Lei nods, waving to the guards as they pass through the second-to-last doorway. They nod back, and Naia is aware of their eyes on her. As she looks back at them, one glares, looks down his nose at her. Naia bares her teeth and turns away, satisfied at his startled expression. The guards forget that Lei doesn't belong to them, to any of the people, but to herself first and foremost.

"Maybe gods fall in love with humans."

"What?" Naia pulls herself from her thoughts, looking at Lei. They've reached the last doorway, the one that separates the Prophet from the balcony, from the people. She can hear the roar behind them, impossibly loud, excited, blessed. They'll be able to see their second sun, bask in her attention, dance under her love. Soon she'll give them all the attention they need until tomorrow, and then the day after that. And the day after that.

"Gods fall in love with humans too." Lei says, turning to stare at Naia.

The bodyguard looks down at her, taken aback by the Prophet's strong gaze, and for a second she sees something in there, something like a secret, like a whisper of a hint.

"Prophet...." Naia starts, but the doors are pulled open, and she ducks back to avoid the crowd seeing her. Either they don't, or have but don't care, because the roar that greets Lei is enormous, and the Prophet beams. The bodyguard can't tell if that knowing spark is still there anymore, but she recognizes it. And why shouldn't she: it's the one that she knows she has when she tells Lei of her prophetic dreams, when she passes the guards in the halls and tells them to double the rotations, when they catch someone trying to sneak into the Prophet's bedchamber in the dead of night.

It's the look that says 'I know something you wish you knew'.

Naia watches from the alcove as Lei steps out onto the balcony, the roar still going. She raises her hands, and as the people quiet, she slips easily, gracefully, into her usual song, the one that starts off all her daily prophecies and messages. All the steps are perfect, all the movements graceful.

Even if they weren't meant to meet every time, in every life, Naia is sure she would fall in love with the Prophet anyway, and be one of those adoring people at her feet.

217

EM, DON'T.

WE DID EVERYTHING WE NEEDED TO DO, AND SURE, NONE OF THOSE THINGS WERE EASY, BUT THEY WERE VALIANT.

WE...

...CHASED THE RED HARE THAT EMERGED FROM THE OAK CHEST...

...OVER RIVERS, AND THROUGH VALLEYS.

AND WHEN WE FINALLY KILLED THE HARE...

IT CHANGED.

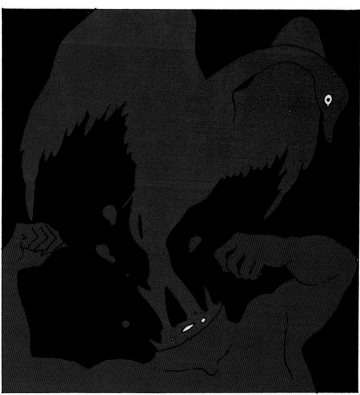

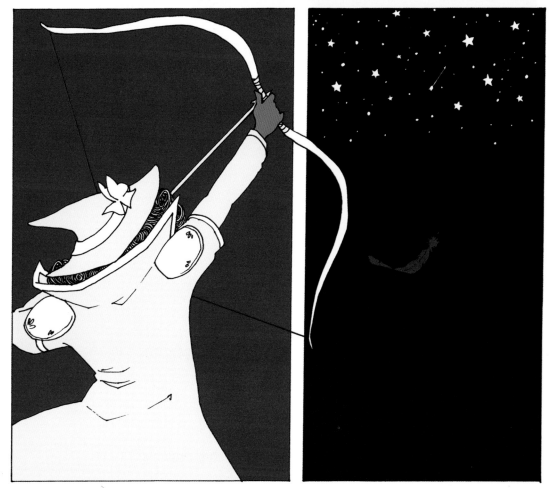

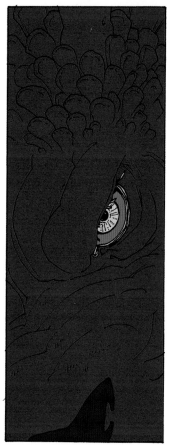

... BUT WE NEVER STOPPED...

... NOT UNTIL WE STRUCK DOWN THE BEAST SAFE-GUARDING LILY'S CRYSTAL HEART.

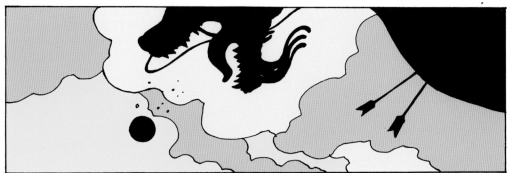

...BUT NOW—

NOW WE KNOW WE CAN WEATHER ANYTHING THAT COMES NEXT. AT BEST, WE'LL HAVE OUR SISTER BACK. AND IF SHE DOESN'T WAKE UP...

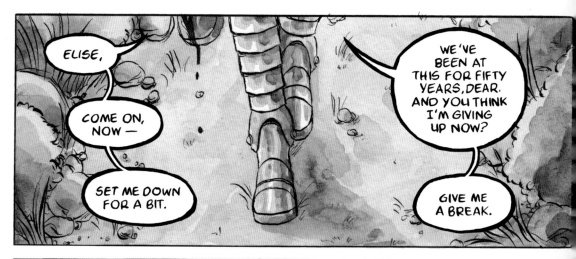

Adventuring

mgglnt

WANTED

BY HIS MAJESTY, KING ANGULIS,
LORD OF THE REALM BY THE ORDER
OF THE DARK CRESCENT

RETURN   ALIVE

DARA OF ROBLES

GUILTY OF TRESPASSING, LIBEL,
LARCENY, ASSAULT, ARSON,
ATTEMPTED MURDER, TREASON,
& UNSANCTIONED USE OF MAGIC.

REWARD OF LORDSHIP

DRAT. we'll have to lie low for a while.

LORDSHIP? really?

WANTED

BY HIS MAJESTY, KING ANGULIS,
LORD OF THE REALM BY THE ORDER
OF THE DARK CRESCENT

RETURN ALIVE

ALVA OF ROBLES

GUILTY OF TRESPASSING, LIBEL,
LARCENY, ASSAULT, ARSON,
ATTEMPTED MURDER, TREASON,
& UNSANCTIONED USE OF MAGIC.

REWARD OF LORDSHIP

DON'T WORRY! I'll make us a glamour spell.

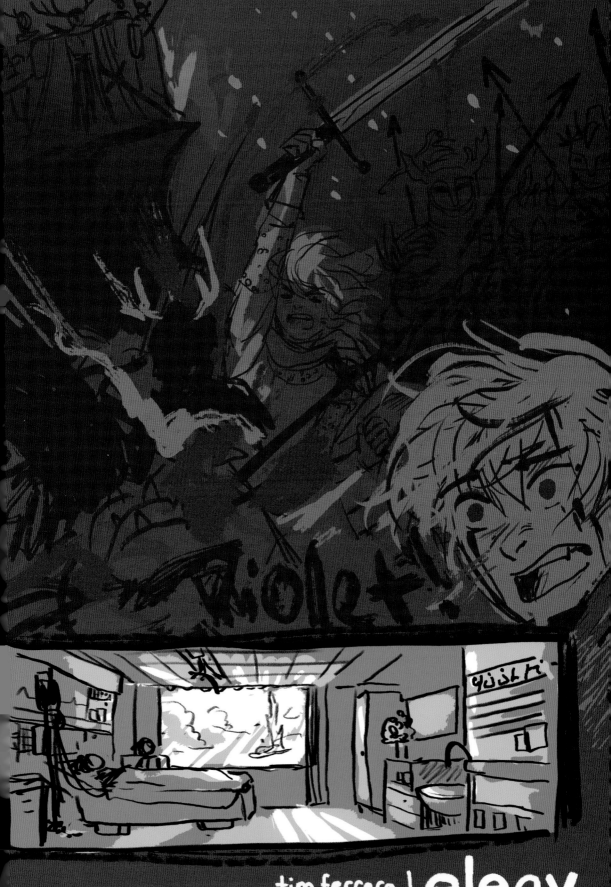

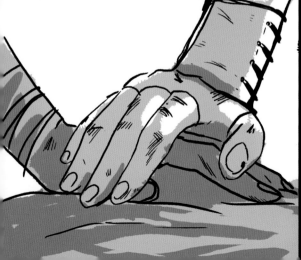

I'm fine. I'll be fine.

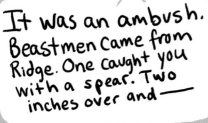

It was an ambush. Beastmen came from Ridge. One caught you with a spear. Two inches over and—

THROB

Right?

To the courageous & fantastic Kickstarter backers whose
generosity and support have made this book a reality,

THANK YOU

All of your names will forever live in our hearts
and at onethousandandoneknights.com/thankyou

MEET THE KNIGHTS

The Knights of Fellowship were asked to define knighthood, how they each gather strength and find sources of inspiration.

★ AME Pg. 91
Courage, hope and perseverance can make the weakest character strong. Courage to find the strength to go forth; hope that the future will be brighter; perseverance to endure the present. That's what I think anyway!

@ameruu   ameru.tumblr.com

ADAMS, LEISL Pg. 26
Leisl Adams is a Storyboard Artist and Illustrator from in Hamilton Ontario, Canada and a Sheridan College Alumni. She has done work in film, television and print, including work for Simon and Schuster, Rubicon Publishing, Arcana Comics, and online comic strips, On The Edge, and Not My Show.

www.leisladams.com   @leisladams   fancymolasses.tumblr.com

ALEGRE, DAVE Pg. 27
Distilled to its simplest components, I define strength as the capacity of a person to uphold what they feel is right—be it physical, mental, or spiritual. A knight is a natural extrapolation of this concept—they are a paragon of strength!

www.scrotumnose.com   @scrotumnose   scrotumnose.tumblr.com

ALVES, MARIANA Pg. 106
A knight is a promise of protection, strength and honor. There are many knights in the world, and not all of them wear shining armor or ride a mighty steed. They can be found in the most unlikely places and come in all shapes and sizes. I'm proud to say I know quite a few, in fact.

www.marianaalvesillustration.carbonmade.com   @serpentshipmate   serpentsshipmate.tumblr.com

AMANN, MYCHAL Pg. 128-132
For me, strength isn't about manliness, muscles, or power over others. When I think of strength I think about what obstacles everyone has to overcome before they can truly feel comfortable with themselves and with others. Having the will power to be able to do battle with personal demons, helping out a stranger in need (even when they might not want it), or even just knowing when to be able to ask friends and family for help when we need it most. Strength is many things, but I find the most powerful strength to be when people are struggling and striving to constantly better not just themselves, but their world around them.

www.mychalamann.com   @swampkips

AN, ANGELA Pg. 40
Strength is being true to yourself and what you believe in. For me, it's being confident in who you are, and the path you choose to take. It is understanding that not everyone thinks or believes the same thing and that's ok

@angelaanthill   angelaan.tumblr.com

AXL99 Pg. 123, 190
All heroes, chosen or reluctant, have one thing beautiful thing in common that they apply to everything they do: their resolve. The resolve to do what they feel is the right thing, to persevere, to find another way to succeed in the face of adversity, to live with their choices. Anyone can be a knight when they are resolute; wonderful things happen when they put their mind to the task and follow through.

www.axl99.net   @axl99   axl99.tumblr.com

BAGUIO, RAMILLE Pg. 72-73
A knight is one that faces adversity regardless of overwhelming circumstance. They can be ferocious, brave, cunning, and even foolhardy. Their strength lies in their unrelenting will to protect others and their ideals.

@secretskull   bargeist.tumblr.com

BENEFIELD, JD Pg. 62–71

For me, what gives me strength and inspiration is having one really well-thought out virtue to strive for and live by as best as possible.

www.randombattlescomic.com   @jd_benefield   jinraoh.tumblr.com

BENNETT, ANDY Pg. 107

Strength to me, is the ability to navigate your day to day life and stay true to who you are. If you find yourself in the minority, its more than likely life will kick you in the balls from time to time. You are a multifaceted person and the rest of humanity probably won't understand every aspect of what makes you happy. So dust yourself off, keep your chin up and cover your groin when necessary.

www.andybennett.info   @mrandybennett   andybennett.tumblr.com

BESSA, RICARDO Pg. 178

Strength is doing what you feel must be done, even if it's not what you WANT to do.

www.ricardobessa.com   @rfbessa   ricardobessa.tumblr.com

BOAKE , ALEX Pg. 39

Tons of muscles! Nah, just kidding, of course. To me, a strong character is one that bounces back when faced with adversity, even if they have to struggle to get there. There are different ways to be strong than just physically, of course, so it's interesting to see characters that show inner power.

www.alexboake.com/blog   @scapegoated   scapegoated.tumblr.com

BRENNAN, MEGAN Pg. 42–45

Obviously strength is about more than just being able to physically lift 15 elephants or whatever! The real kind of strength comes from really knowing yourself and being capable of dealing with tough situations. I keep wishing I was a stronger person! But then again, if I knew that I was able to lift 15 elephants, I would feel pretty capable and confident.

www.megan-brennan.com   @megthebrennan   megthebrennan.tumblr.com

CASTLE, TRUDI Pg. 24

Being friendly and concerned for others no matter how you're feeling, with back up coffee/tea and donuts!

www.trudiart.com   @trudicastle   ladytruds.tumblr.com

CHU Pg. 46–47

Strength is pulled from belief in one's convictions. However, this strength does not discern between good or evil, nor does it guarantee victory. It is simply the energy needed to fuel people on their chosen path through life. Like how pizza helps comic artists draw.

www.raizap.com   @sdamned   hyenafu.tumblr.com

CLIFF, TERRANA Pg. 117

Even a slug like me can be a knight. The forest ecosystem needs protection from invasive (and delicious) plants.

Is that a creeping kudzu I hear? Yum, yum!

www.nwain.com   @terranacliff   terranacliff.tumblr.com

COZENS, DANE Pg. 124–125

It takes a strong-willed person to ride a cat, and Pipi is that kinda person. She had always been strong-willed...so strong that she intimidated most men. So due to circumstance, Pipi became tougher. As one of the few people tough enough to discipline and ride a tabby cat, she is one of the most capable people to take care of herself in the badlands. If you were to ask her what makes her so strong, she wouldn't really know what to say. I suppose she never bothered trying to prove her value and always tries to be self-sufficient.

danecozens.com

CRAIG, LESLIE Pg. 49–57

It took me a long time to decide what a Knight was to me. A Knight doesn't have to be a man. Doesn't have to be part of a 'Round Table' or someone who lives in Legend. It just has to be someone who has the courage to step forward when others can't

www.lesliecraig.co.uk   @lj_craig   lesliecraig.tumblr.com

FERRARA, TIM Pg. 241–251

How do we measure what counts as strength when everyone is so different? For some, it may be fighting for their beliefs. For others, perhaps saying no when everyone else is saying yes. It could be standing up for those who can't stand up for themselves, or having the courage to do what's right instead of what's easy. Or maybe strength is to admit when we're wrong, to put others first, to have the capacity and the willingness to change. Strength is something we find together, because the truth is that we're not so different after all.

www.odecomic.com @alittlekings

FONG, GRACE Pg. 92–93

The hardest part of building inner confidence is realizing so much of how we see ourselves is what others told us how to think.

www.gracepfong.com @gpfong fictograph.tumblr.com

GEOGHEGAN, BARBARA Pg. 60–61

To me, a strong character is someone who inspires me to live my life to the fullest, whether it's a warrior princess or a scullery maid.

www.barbaragdraws.com @barbarabot barbarabot.tumblr.com

GORGONIST, THE Pg. 94–97

When I found out that knights actually fought to protect the interests of the strongest and most powerful people in the land, rather than to protect the weak, everything I thought I knew came crashing down. So my story is about the kind of knight I want to believe in, those who come from the bottom, who fight for the oppressed masses, even if no one else cares. It is a fantasy that may come true.

www.thegorgonist.etsy.com @thegorgonist thegorgonist.tumblr.com

GRABOWSKI, JOSEPH Pg. 157–161

A Knight stays cool. Cooler heads prevail.

www.spiritscomic.com @joeygeewhiz

GUSTAFSSON, NICOLE Pg. 12

One of the best ways for me to find strength and inspiration is to immerse myself in our world. Whether it is traveling to a new city, exploring my own backyard, or even reading a great book, it's these little everyday discoveries that help me grow in strength as a person and brings inspiration to my day.

www.nimasprout.com @nimasprout nimasprout.tumblr.com

HANDWERKER, KORI MICHELE Pg. 234–235

To me, real strength is to have integrity. There's nothing stronger, and few things more frightening, than doing the right thing when no one is watching.

www.korimichele.com @korimichele koricomics.tumblr.com

HOGAN, ZOEY Pg. 237

A Knight, to me, is someone who uses their strength for the good of others. This doesn't have to be physical strength! We all have strengths, and we're all knights if we use them to defend and improve the lives of those around us.

www.caporushes.com @caporushes

HUNSHER, C. S. Pg. 80–90

"What does strength mean to me?" To be able to stand up for what you believe in, and protect the ones you care for in the face of adversary. To not compromise yourself even when everyone around you is going in a different direction. To be able to face each day with a smile or even just get out of bed at all. To be kind to those who would hurt you.

irlmedusa.tumblr.com @acarrottweets

HURLEY, JESS Pg. 98–102

Strength is more than being able to lift great weights or going undefeated in battle. It is doing what you think is right and being able to handle when you are wrong.

www.giraffejess.portfoliobox.net @jessjulitz artbyjessjulitz.tumblr.com

JAIMONSTER Pg. 128–132

A Knight's strength doesn't come from what they do for themselves, but from what they do for others.

www.jaimonster.com @Jaimonster jaimonster.tumblr.com

KAHN, RACHEL Pg. 120–122

I think knights are leaders, people whose role is to be more of a symbol at the front of something than necessarily the best warriors. So, as leaders, knightly strength is found in learning the strengths of others, helping others be strong, inspiring and enabling those around you.

www.wealdcomics.com @portablecity portablecity.tumblr.com

KALEGIRO Pg. 75–77

No matter how big or small your inner battle may seem, I think we all go through some of the same things. Feelings of helplessness, weakness, loneliness. I also think we all have the choice to fight. We are all warriors and knights in our own way, and we all have the strength inside us to fight. We can choose to stand and challenge what's wrong, even when we don't think it will make a difference. When we try, it already has.

www.kalegiro.com @kalegiro kalegiro.tumblr.com

KAWAKAMI, ERI Pg. 184–185

A knight has to be brave, strong, and kind. Brave doesn't mean that you aren't afraid, but you're willing to face the fears you do have. Strong doesn't mean you win every battle, but you'll do your best and accept what you have and who you are. Kind means that you try to understand others and fight for them. It doesn't matter how old you are, or where you've come from, or what you've done in the past; anyone can be a knight.

www.eri-kawakami.com @erikawakamiArt eri-kawakami.tumblr.com

KIM, MINKI Pg. 128–132

Accepting my weaknesses and striving toward improvement to me exemplifies strength. An invincible knight understands all of her weaknesses while a heroic one still reaches through bramble and flames to support a friend or stranger. I owe my life to many knights and I vow to be a great one myself.

www.ctale.thecomicseries.com @froncentrate

LAVIGNE, JULIA Pg. 156

Like most artists, I can find inspiration everywhere but I love to look back on my childhood idols and interests. This piece was inspired by beautiful fairy wallpaper that adorned the walls in my childhood bedroom. These wallpaper fairies lived among the flowers and I liked to imagine they protected the bees that lived and survived off of the flowers in the garden. I was so excited about creating a lady knight protagonist based off of these fairies; one that will inspire children to love bees and our fragile ecosystem.

www.floating-heads.net @julia_lavigne

LAWLER, COLIN Pg. 157–161

A Knight is capable of wearing whatever hat is required of him/her, so to speak.

www.colinlawler.com @drawingupastorm clawler.tumblr.com

LINFIELD, STU Pg. 74, 177

Strength means the bravery to face your fears and obstacles that may seem insurmountable.

www.stulinfield.com @stulinfield

LIU, LANNY Pg. 146–155

A fierce determination to reach their goal, even if it means making enemies, makes a strong character.

www.lannyworld.com @lannyliu lannydraws.tumblr.com

LONGUA, KATIE Pg. 144–145, 212–213

Strength is having the will and courage to explore even the darkest places of our universe!

www.klongua.com @katiesaurusrex klongua.tumblr.com

MAJOR, CHRISTINA Pg. 110-116

There is an amazing strength in finding connection and wonder in isolating and difficult times. Even if they feel like they're not winning their own battles, the "knights" who inspire others to seek their goals are so important. Thanks to everyone who has fought for me. I hope I can return the favor!

www.horizonscape.com @delphina2k delphina2k.tumblr.com

MANOMIVIBUL, MICHAEL Pg. 126-127

What is bravery without a little stupidity? What is chivalry without a little arrogance? Knights are a concept full of contradictions. At the core of any knight is the desire to always be better, do better. That is why I love them

www.mikemanoart.com @mikemanoart mikemanoart.tumblr.com

MARTINET, KJ Pg. 108-109

Perseverance.

www.kjmartinet.com @kjmartinet kjmartinet.tumblr.com

MAYANI, RAFAEL Pg. 133, 240

Strength is: Standing up for what you believe in, which in my opinion is one of the hardest things to do at times. This is true for anything from cereal for breakfast to slaying the dragon to rescue the princess.

www.rafaelmayani.com @rmayani rafaeldraws.tumblr.com

MCKENZIE, JOSH Pg. 163

The most important part of being a dragon rider is always remembering that at any time, your dragon can buck, or you can slip, and you can fall to the earth and that'll be the end of you. This is why dragon riders never fly alone. Although our dragons and training are formidable, the true strength of a rider are the friends they've made and the friends they fly with. These are our best asset, and the one we can rely on the most when things get rough. These are our true valuables

www.joshmckenzieart.com @amonns amonstar.tumblr.com

MELANCON, ISABELLE Pg. 119

What is a knight - A knight is anyone protecting the weak, the forgotten, the lost. It is anyone bearing armor, or steel, leather or skin. It is anyone who wields a shield or a blade in defense of those who need it, may it be shaped from metal or magic or words. A knight is a story we can't forget.

www.namesakecomic.com @secondlina secondlina.tumblr.com

MENDOZA, MOLLY Pg. 164

She is strong and she is powerful — she is our hero, she is our escape. She also sweats, bleeds, scrapes her knees. She also grows tired, breaks down, regrets, and worries. She also crumples, and fails, and cries — But she is strong and she is powerful: Our hero our reality.

www.mollymendoza.com @fussfusspot msmollym.tumblr.com

MILLER, CATHERINE M. Pg. 165

A person who offers protection to those unable to do so themselves.

@encregris coldpress.tumblr.com

MILLER, KELLY LEIGH Pg. 16-23

For me, what makes a character strong is their ability to work through a tough situation even if they are hurt or scared. Most people perceive strength as a physical thing, which it can be, but I believe true strength comes from within.

www.kellyleighmiller.com @bookofkellz kellyleighmiller.tumblr.com

NEGRETE, MAGGIE LYNN Pg. 238-239

Strength is seeing your weaknesses as places of growth and learning.

www. mgglntcreates.com @mgglnt

NEHLAWI, SOFIA Pg. 134–139, 166–171, 206–211
Someone willing to risk what they know for the unknown, willing to look the impossible in the eye and tell it that they'll beat it today, for the sake of another. The ultimate shield and ultimate sword, doing whatever they must to defend who needs it most, regardless of personal feelings.

mooseyfate.tumblr.com

NEMES, CLAIRE Pg. 13
For me, there is no better inspiration than a long walk alone in the woods; it's also a good reminder that Mother Nature is stronger than all of us. The smallest beetle and most towering tree, the staunchest ally and the most stalwart enemy, are all at the mercy of the same forces. Paradoxically, this is a fortifying thought!

www.cnemes.blogspot.com   instagram.com/cenemes

O'DONNELL, SARAH Pg. 28–38
A person cursed with a loyal spirit and reckless devotion. Someone who falters, but the thought of turning back hasn't once crossed their mind. A lovely person who will do anything for others if it means they need not think of themselves.

www. everydayfoxlife.itch.io   @everydayfoxlife everydayfoxlife.tumblr.com

OSTERTAG, MOLLY Pg. 48
A knight can recognize the strength within herself and seeks out causes and people to devote it to. She works every day to be better and to find places in the world where her particular talents are needed.

www.mollyostertag.com   @mollyostertag mollyostertag.tumblr

OVERSTREET, JEN Pg. 58–59, 118, 179
A knight dedicates themselves to a purpose greater than themselves. Knighthood is about individuals going beyond personal success to find fellowship revolving a common ideal — whether it's a quest, a moral code, or a leader and her goals.

www.streetoverjen.com   @streetoverjen

PANDYA, AATMAJA Pg. 182
Ever since I was young, I've preferred depictions of strength that emphasize self-control and strong willpower over the ability to commit great violence. I love characters that fight because they have to, not because they want to — people who fight because they have something they want to protect, or have a goal to achieve, or because no one else will do what needs to be done.

www.aatmajapandya.com   @aymayjay aatmajapandya.tumblr.com

PEGAN, JIMM Pg. 104–105
"Knight" as a word has many definitions and carries with it as many qualities: Honor, bravery, chivalry, and nobility are all part of the package. But for me, the trait that marks a True Knight and makes her a character worthy of aspiration is her loyalty; whether to her friends, her lord, or her own values.

@jpegan jpegtwopointoh.tumblr.com

PIETSCH, CAREY Pg. 192 - 203
A knight is more than a sword! Knights approach problems with empathy and respect. They work to help others, but know to take care of themselves and make their own needs known as well.

www.careydraws.com   @careydraws careydraws.tumblr.com

PINKIMOON Pg. 232–233
Strength is made of Courage, Faith and, most importantly, Love. There are times when one can be fragile like a flower, either physically or emotionally, but even the delicate flower can be strong when faced with obstacles. Strength is the courage to face the obstacles. Strength is having faith to overcome it. The great strength of love, reminds us how we are not alone. Love gives us the strength to endure it all.

www.pinkimoon.com   @pinkimoon

RAMDIAL, SAYADA Pg. 14–15
A knight is one who seeks to defend those who can't defend themselves. Whether it's a traditional knight in shining armor, defending their kingdom, or a woman in a pink sari, standing up to her neighbour's abusive husband with a bamboo sword, a knight protects with honour.

www.sayadaramdial.com   @sayadaramdial sayadaramdial.tumblr.com

REINWAND, PAUL Pg. 172-175, 183

Strength comes from conviction! Strength can stem just as readily from cool logic as from a fiery heart. A strong character has the determination to follow and forge their own path, regardless of the morality.

www.konradwerks.com @paulreinwand konradwerks.tumblr.com

REL Pg. 186-189

A good knight should endeavor to remain both valorous and undoomed.

www.relissoawesome.com @relemenopy relemenopy.tumblr.com

REM Pg. 41

To me, a person with true strength is someone who can fight and protect their own beliefs, while still lifting up and supporting those around them. Strength doesn't just come from within, but also grows from the bonds people share with others.

www.devilscandycomic.com @tsulala

SCOTT, OLIVER Pg. 204-205, 226-227

'For the strength question, I think strength is about being able to admit when you're wrong, to see your flaws and try to do something to change things for the better. Loving yourself and the people around you will make you strong.

cloodiedraws.tumblr.com

SCOTT, JULIA Pg. 25

"The strength that resides in contemplation Bathes me in silver starlight I will lead this beast on a chain of flowers Fear not the jaws that devour soul" -Queen of the Borrowed Light (Diadem of 12 stars) WOLVES IN THE THRONE ROOM

www.telepath-generation.com @drooliasnott inkdrinker.tumblr.com

SEKI, MASAE Pg. 10-11

Friends and family... that is where I find countless inspiration and gain strength from. Without them, I would not be the person I am today. I feel fearless when I am with the people I love. Even in the most difficult times where impossible obstacles lie ahead, I can count on them to give me a hand. It gives me strength knowing that there are people I love who will watch my back and catch me when I fall. From them I learned what it takes to be strong, brave and fearless... like a knight.

www. masaeseki.artstation.com @masaeseki saesaeseki.tumblr.com

SHAFFER, DANIEL Pg. 180-181

I think strength is a combination of perseverance and honesty with yourself. It's the ability to make yourself keep going and the ability to stop and think critically about your actions.

www.daniel-shaffer.com @DanielHShaffer danielhshaffer.tumblr.com

SILVA, DASHIELL Pg. 78-79, 176

To me, a character's strong if you can imagine them doing something banal like laundry as well as doing something exciting like slaying a crazed gryphon before it demolishes an alms house. if you can picture someone being both boring and heroic then you know they're well defined.

www.dashiellsilva.com @dashiellsilva linesdamnlines.tumblr.com

SIMES, SARAH Pg. 191

Pursuing what you passionately believe in is the mark of true knighthood.

www.sarahsimes.com @allaloam

STOLL, ANNIE Pg. 241-251

Strength is knowing yourself. It's holding true to what you believe in, even in the face of great odds. When the whole world feels against you, know that you are not alone. Listen to your heart. Your voice has power. A wise wizard once said "It takes a great deal of courage to stand up to your enemies, but a great deal more to stand up to your friends." We are all knights.

www.anniestoll.com @aniistoll odecomic.com

TAN, CHARLES Pg. 140-141

A Knight is a person who puts others before themselves. And a Knight is full of love, for "...love suffers long and is kind; love does not envy; love does not parade itself, is not puffed up; does not behave rudely, does not seek its own, is not provoked, thinks no evil; does not rejoice in iniquity, but rejoices in the truth; bears all things, believes all things, hopes all things, endures all things" (New King James Version, 1 Cor. 13. 4-13).

www.behance.net/charlestan @charlestan charlestan.tumblr.com

THOMPSON, SALLY JANE Pg. 214-215, 228-230

Strength comes out in the choosing of the (sometimes hard, scary) right thing — the thing that helps, protects, and persists — over the (easy, attractive) path of least resistance.

www.sallyjanethompson.co.uk @sallythompson

TRUNGLES Pg. 216-225

You can find strength and inspiration in the sweet little things to help you through the big and the bitter things! I'm a firm believer in taking selfish little moments to make it through long challenges.

www.trungles.com @trungles artoftrungles.tumblr.com

TUYA, JEZ Pg. 236

Any of us can become a knight. It is a matter of standing up not just yourself, but for the plights of others. It is not about swords, sorcery or fancy armor but rather about what you can do to become that person others can rely on. We can all be knights.

www.behance.net/jeztuya @jez_tuya

VENUSJAW Pg. 162

There are so many different ways to be strong. Though, I think the most rewarding strength comes from the acceptance of ourselves and others through and despite adversities we face.

www.etsy.com/shop/venusjaw

WEATHERS, JABARI Pg 142-143

The last five and a half years have shown me an abundance of great strength from the women, men and people that I've come to know through my art, and I've learned an invaluable amount from them. It takes a lot to survive as an outcast. That willpower is certainly a kind of strength, but the courage to make work and to be yourself, share your messages and experiences with a world that in many ways doesn't want it but certainly needs to witness it is the definition of strength that is most important to me. Strength does not have one meaning for me, but this meaning of strength has been the most applicable to my life, and the examples of it that I've learned from have had the most impact on me.

www.jmwillustration.com @jabariweathers fortuneandfey.tumblr.com

WINTER, LILITH Pg. 103

A knight, anyone who is brave enough to fight for what they believe in. A person who lives to protect the weak. Noble, smart, and kind.

www.furaffinity.net/user/lilithrose lilithwinter.tumblr.com/

XU, NICOLE Pg. 231

A knight has perseverance and integrity, is someone who never lets go of what they treasure.

www.nicole-xu.com @nicolexu_ nicole-xu.tumblr.com

Dear Reader,

Thank you for picking up this book. There are 1001 characters over the course of three volumes that make up 1001 Knights. The book in your hands is the second — **FELLOWSHIP**. Every artist and Kickstarter backer are knights and now by finishing this book, you are a part of this dialogue too.

Art can change us and inspire us to do great things. Now that you have read these stories, you can go forth and make the world a better place. Share this book, support and check out the 1001 Knights artists. You are always welcome in the 1001 Knights community.

RISE A KNIGHT.